Disney

Family Story Collection

S0-AWL-428

Honesty Is the Best Policy

STORIES ABOUT INTEGRITY

Book Seven

Collection copyright © 2005 Disney Enterprises, Inc.

All rights reserved. No part of this book may be reproduced or
transmitted in any form or by any means, electronic or mechanical,
including photocopying, recording, or by any information storage
and retrieval system, without written permission from the publisher.
For information address Disney Press,
114 Fifth Avenue, New York, New York 10011-5690.

Printed in China
First Edition
1 3 5 7 9 10 8 6 4 2

ISBN 0-7868-3531-1

For more Disney Press fun, visit www.disneybooks.com

Book Seven

Honesty Is the
Best Policy

STORIES ABOUT INTEGRITY

Introduction

Sometimes it is difficult for children to distinguish between right and wrong. Their first instinct is often to give the answer that reflects best on themselves, even if this answer is not always the truth. It's important to teach children not to put their own needs above everyone else's. Although the short-term advantage is obvious, in the long run, honesty will have a much greater impact on everyone's life.

In "Jane's Big Mistake," Jane lets her anger with Peter Pan cloud her judgment. She learns a hard lesson but realizes that loyalty to her true friends is the only choice after all. In "Making Peace," Pocahontas positions herself as a peacemaker by serving as her people's ambassador to England. Pocahontas isn't thinking of herself, but rather of the benefits to her tribe.

Jane's Big Mistake

from *Peter Pan in Return to Never Land*

Don't let anger lead you to do the wrong thing.

After Peter Pan saved Jane from Captain Hook, who had kidnapped her right out of her London bedroom, he took her to the Lost Boys' hideout. Jane had heard all about Peter Pan and the Lost Boys from her mother, Wendy. But she had stopped believing. Now, she realized that they were real!

However, Jane was a serious girl.

It wasn't long before she got tired of the boys' childish games and pranks. She had to get home.

"The only way out of here is to fly," Peter Pan told her.

Jane tried to fly, but she wasn't very good at it. On her final attempt, when she fell to the ground, her special notebook tumbled out of her pocket.

"Hey, what's this?" asked Peter as he picked it up.

"Oh, give it back. It's my list of things to do, places to be—important things," said Jane.

Peter didn't think that sounded like fun. "Keep away from Jane!" he cried. The Lost Boys began tossing the notebook around playfully. They kept at it until Cubby accidentally swallowed the notebook whole.

"Oh, grow up!" Jane yelled furiously. "You're a bunch of ridiculous children!" And with that, she stomped off into the woods.

Meanwhile, Captain Hook had been waiting for a chance to use Jane to get to Peter Pan.

"Peter stole my treasure, and my men would mutiny if I so much as tried to leave without it," he told her. "I'll give you passage home on my ship if you help me recover my treasure. The treasure is useless to Peter. He's not

sensible like us. He's just a boy who'll never grow up."

Hook's words stirred up all of the anger Jane had felt before. She forgot that Hook was not trustworthy and accepted his proposal. He gave her a whistle to blow as a signal that she'd found the treasure.

Soon Jane came upon Peter and the Lost Boys. She felt uneasy about tricking them, but she still hadn't forgotten their teasing. "Why don't we play a game?" Jane suggested. "Like maybe . . . treasure hunt?"

Peter agreed, on the condition that Jane try both to think like and have fun like a Lost Boy. Before Jane knew it, that's exactly what she was doing. Peter showed her all around the island. It was wonderful! She soon forgot all about being angry.

Then, Jane peeked into a small cave. "The treasure! I found—" she started to say, but then she remembered her deal with Hook.

Immediately, she realized she had made a mistake. She had let her anger and frustration cloud her judgment. Peter Pan and the Lost Boys were her friends. She couldn't betray them. Jane took the whistle out of her pocket and threw it into the water. She never forgot the important lesson she had learned.

Making Peace

from *Pocahontas II: Journey to a New World*

Choose reason over rage.

ohn Rolfe and his crew were just arriving in a new land. They had sailed from England at the command of King James to help resolve tensions between the settlers of Jamestown and the Indians.

The Indian princess Pocahontas stood among the crowd of settlers gathered at the dock to greet the ship. In the nearby woods, her people, hidden and armed, were quietly watching.

As Rolfe rode his horse down the gangplank, a settler bumped into Pocahontas.

Just then, Rolfe's horse panicked. It reared up, threw Rolfe to the ground, and galloped dangerously through the crowd. The settler who had bumped into Pocahontas had his back turned to the charging horse—and he was about to be trampled! Pocahontas dove toward the settler, knocking him out of the way seconds before the horse thundered by.

But the settler never saw the horse. He was

furious about being pushed and started
toward Pocahontas.

Immediately, the Indians in the woods

revealed themselves and drew their bows. The startled settlers raised their muskets in return.

A battle was about to erupt. Without thinking of her own safety, Pocahontas placed herself between the two sides. "No, wait!" she called out, raising her arms.

Pocahontas knew it was wrong to fight all of the settlers because of the bad behavior of one man. It would only lead to more anger and bloodshed. Her people lowered their weapons. Rolfe raised his hand, and the settlers put down their arms, too.

That evening, Rolfe went to the tribal village to

meet with the chief. He stood before Chief Powhatan and spoke, as the rest of the tribe listened. He explained his mission.

"To build trust, I would like you to sail back with me, to meet my king," Rolfe said.

"I don't want your chief's land. He wants mine. Why doesn't he cross the Salt Water to see *me?*" Powhatan replied.

The tribe's resentment began to swell.

"You want our land," one of the Indians said to Rolfe. "You mean to—"

But Pocahontas interrupted him. "Father," she said, turning to Powhatan, "someone must go." She volunteered herself. She couldn't allow anger to cloud their judgment. The tribe needed to know the facts if the fighting were ever to stop.

At first, the tribe thought Pocahontas was being disloyal and siding with the settlers. But Powhatan saw the wisdom of Pocahontas's position. In order for there to be peace, the two sides must understand each other.

It was decided that Pocahontas would sail to England to meet King James. The fate of her people, and of Jamestown, was in her hands.